Have a Ball, Snoopy

Selected cartoons from IF BEAGLES COULD FLY

Charles M. Schulz

CORONET BOOKS
Hodder and Stoughton

PEANUTS COMIC STRIPS
by Charles M. Schulz

Copyright © 1990 by United Feature Syndicate, Inc.

First published in the United States of America 1991
by Ballantine Books

First published in Great Britain in 1993 by
Hodder and Stoughton, a division of Hodder Headline PLC.

This book comprises portions of IF BEAGLES COULD FLY
and is reprinted by arrangement with Ballantine Books

1 3 5 7 9 10 8 6 4 2

ISBN 0 340 58328 2

Printed and bound in Great Britain by
Cox & Wyman Ltd, Reading, Berkshire

Hodder and Stoughton Ltd
A Division of Hodder Headline PLC
47 Bedford Square
London WC1B 3DP

Have a Ball,
SNOOPY!

THEN YOU STARE AT IT UNTIL IT ROLLS ACROSS THE YARD, UP THE STEPS AND INTO THE KITCHEN!

HOW DID A SUPPER DISH GET IN HERE?

BUT YOU HAVE TO KNOW HOW TO DO IT..

8-30

GRAMPA SAYS THE MULTIPLICATION TABLE IS DISAPPEARING FROM HIS HEAD...

NINE TIMES EIGHT IS COMPLETELY GONE..

EIGHT TIMES SIX IS FADING...

HE SAYS HE'S LIVING IN THE LOW NUMBERS

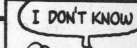

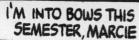

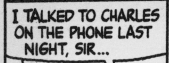

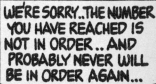

TODAY IS "GRANDPARENTS DAY"

YOU KNOW WHAT I ALWAYS REMEMBER ABOUT MY GRAMPA? HIS JOKE!

HE HAD ONE JOKE, AND IN THE EVENING WHEN WE'D ALL SIT AROUND AT THE DAISY HILL PUPPY FARM, HE'D TELL HIS JOKE..

"WHO WAS THAT BEAGLE I SAW YOU WITH LAST NIGHT? THAT WAS NO BEAGLE, THAT WAS A BAGEL!"

I NEED TWO VOLUNTEERS

SEE THIS? THIS IS WHAT WE CALL A "TARP"

NOW, IF IT STARTS TO RAIN, YOUR JOB IS TO RUSH OUT HERE AND COVER THE INFIELD AND THE PITCHER'S MOUND WITH THIS TARP, OKAY?

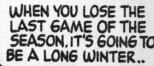

ME?

9-28

NO, MA'AM, I WASN'T GIVING THE ANSWERS...

I WAS JUST LEAKING INFORMATION..

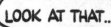

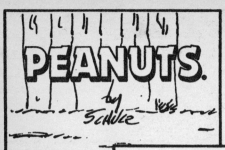

CHARLIE BROWNNN...

I'LL HOLD THE BALL, CHARLIE BROWN, AND YOU COME RUNNING UP AND KICK IT..

AREN'T YOU STARTING IN KIND OF EARLY?

WELL, I HAVE A LOT OF THINGS TO DO..MY APPOINTMENT BOOK IS JUST ABOUT FILLED...

THIS IS THE ONLY TIME I CAN REALLY FIT YOU IN..

I GUESS EVERYBODY IS BUSY THESE DAYS...

10-6

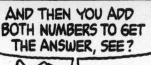

SOME FRIENDS OF OUR FAMILY JUST HAD A NEW BABY...

THEY'RE GREAT HOCKEY FANS SO THEY WANTED TO NAME THE BABY AFTER A HOCKEY PLAYER..

10-26

THEY THOUGHT OF GORDIE HOWE, AND BOBBY HULL AND WAYNE GRETZKY, BUT THEY COULDN'T DECIDE...

SO WHAT DID THEY FINALLY CALL HIM?

ZAMBONI!

→

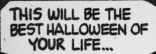

PEANUTS.

by SCHULZ

YES, MA'AM, I'M READY WHEN YOU ARE..

WAIT 'TIL SHE HEARS ME READ THIS REPORT, MARCIE...I'LL GET THE BEST GRADE SHE'S EVER GIVEN!

11-1

STAND UP! A DOG IS SUPPOSED TO SALUTE WHEN A HUMAN WALKS BY!

SORRY

I THOUGHT YOU WEREN'T REQUIRED TO SALUTE IF YOU WEREN'T IN UNIFORM...

HERE'S THE WORLD FAMOUS SURGEON READY TO TAKE CARE OF ANY INJURIES THAT MAY OCCUR DURING THE GAME...

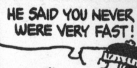

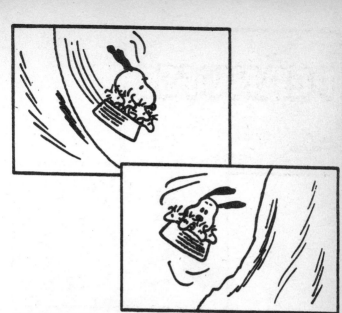

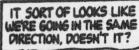

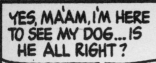

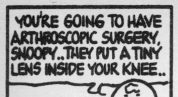

HELLO? THIS IS MARCIE..MAY I SPEAK TO CHARLES, PLEASE?

HE JUST CALLED FROM THE HOSPITAL..HIS STUPID DOG HURT HIMSELF PLAYING HOCKEY..WHAT'S A DOG DOING PLAYING HOCKEY?

MY GRAMPA IS SIXTY-FIVE, AND HE PLAYS HOCKEY..

11-21

HE MUST BE SOME BEAGLE!

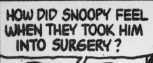